Missing Pieces
Level One

MW00954660

Name

Date

■ Choose the piece that fits. Write a check mark (✓) above the picture.

To parents
Guide your child to write his or her name and date in the box above. Do the exercise along with your child if he or she has difficulty.

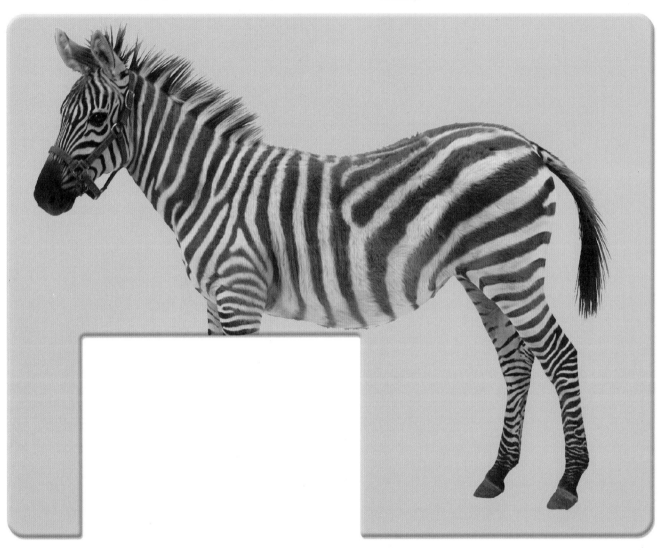

( )

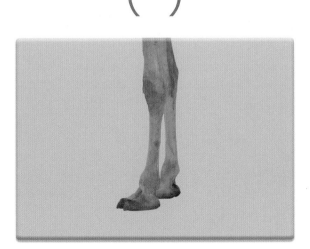

( )

1

■ Choose the piece that fits. Write a check mark (✓) above the picture.

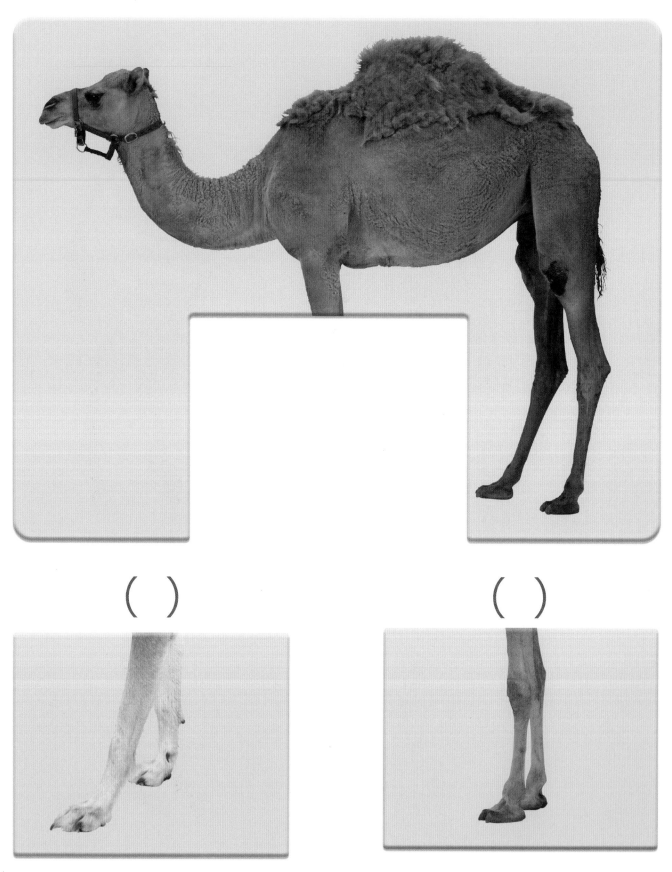

( )   ( )

Missing Pieces
Level Two

Name

Date

■ Choose the piece that fits. Write a check mark (✓) above the picture.

To parents
Encourage your child to look carefully at the shapes of the pieces.

( )

( )

■ Choose the piece that fits. Write a check mark (✓) above the picture.

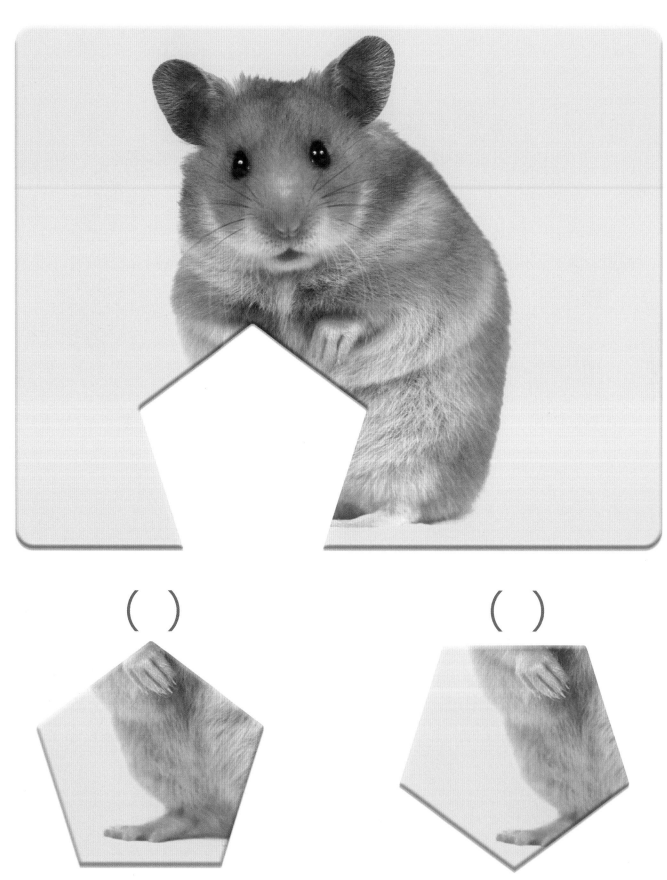

( )   ( )

Missing Pieces
Level Three

Name

Date

■ Choose the piece that fits. Write a
check mark (✓) above the picture.

To parents
Encourage your child to look carefully at the pictures on the pieces.

( )   ( )   ( )

■ Choose the piece that fits. Write a check mark (✓) above the picture.

( )   ( )   ( )

Missing Pieces
Level Four

Name

Date

■ Choose the piece that fits. Write a check mark (✓) above the picture.

To parents
Encourage your child to look carefully at the shapes of the pieces.

( ) ( ) ( )

7

■ Choose the piece that fits. Write a check mark (✓) above the picture.

( )   ( )   ( )   ( )

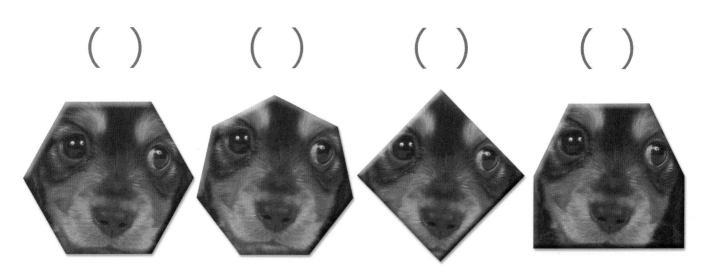

Missing Pieces
Level Five

■ Choose the piece that fits. Write a check mark (✓) above the picture.

To parents
If your child has difficulty, encourage him or her to describe what the missing part of the picture might look like.

( )　　　( )　　　( )　　　( )

9

■ Choose the piece that fits. Write a check mark (✓) above the picture.

( ) ( ) ( ) ( )

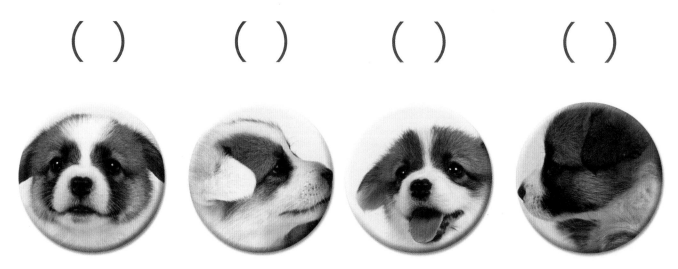

Missing Pieces
Level Six

■ Choose the piece that fits. Write a check mark (✓) above the picture.

To parents
Counting the sides of each piece will help your child find the correct piece.

( )　　　　( )　　　　( )　　　　( )

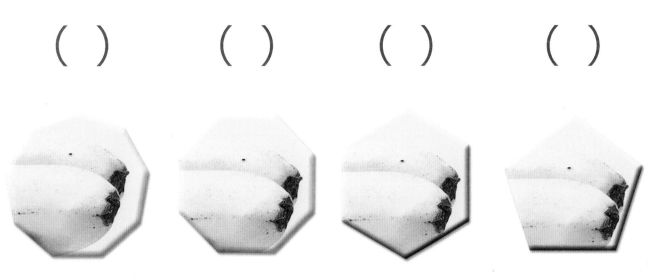

■ Choose the piece that fits. Write a check mark (✓) above the picture.

( )　　　　( )　　　　( )　　　　( )

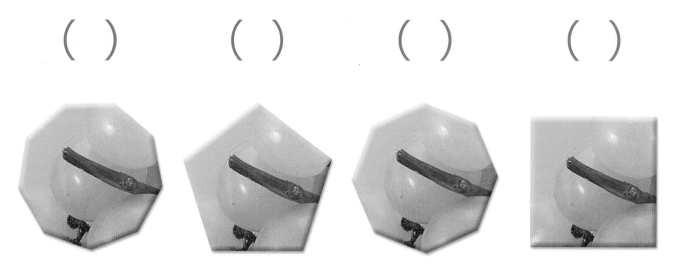

Missing Pieces
Level Seven

■ Choose the piece that fits. Write a check mark (✓) above the picture.

To parents
Looking at the shapes of the pieces carefully will help your child find the correct piece.

( )   ( )   ( )   ( )

■ Choose the piece that fits. Write a check mark (✓) above the picture.

( )　　　　( )　　　　( )　　　　( )

Missing Pieces
Level Eight

Name

Date

■ Choose the piece that fits. Write a check mark (✓) above the picture.

To parents
If your child has difficulty with this activity, look at the shape of each puzzle piece with your child. Together, describe the shapes that you see.

( )　　　　　( )　　　　　( )

( )　　　　　( )　　　　　( )

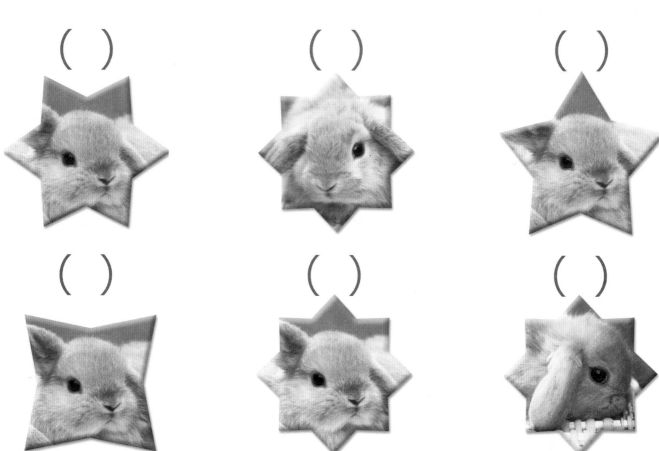

■ Choose the piece that fits. Write a check mark (✓) above the picture.

( )   ( )   ( )

( )   ( )   ( )

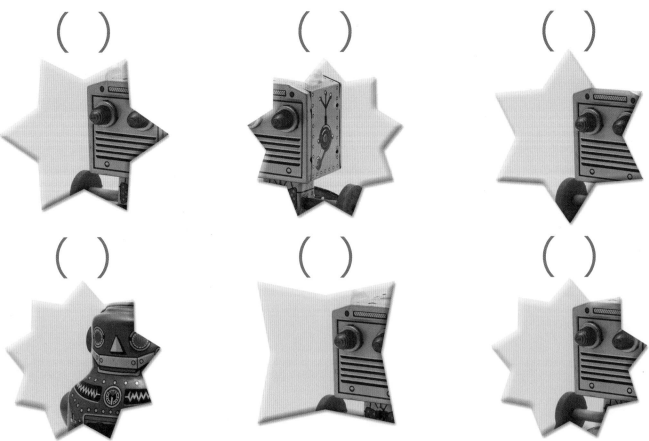

 **Jigsaw Puzzles**
Level One

■ Draw a line to the piece that fits.

Name

Date

To parents
Looking at the illustrations will help your child match the
correct pieces.

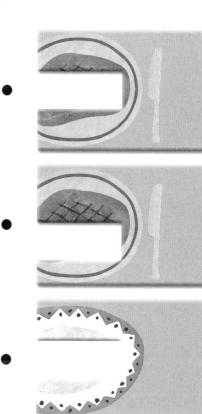

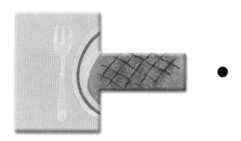

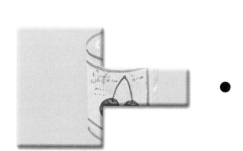

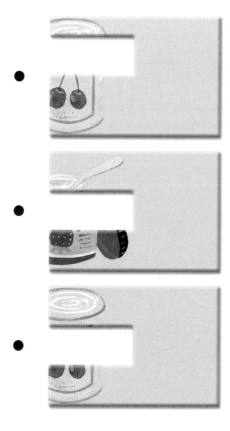

■ Draw a line to the piece that fits.

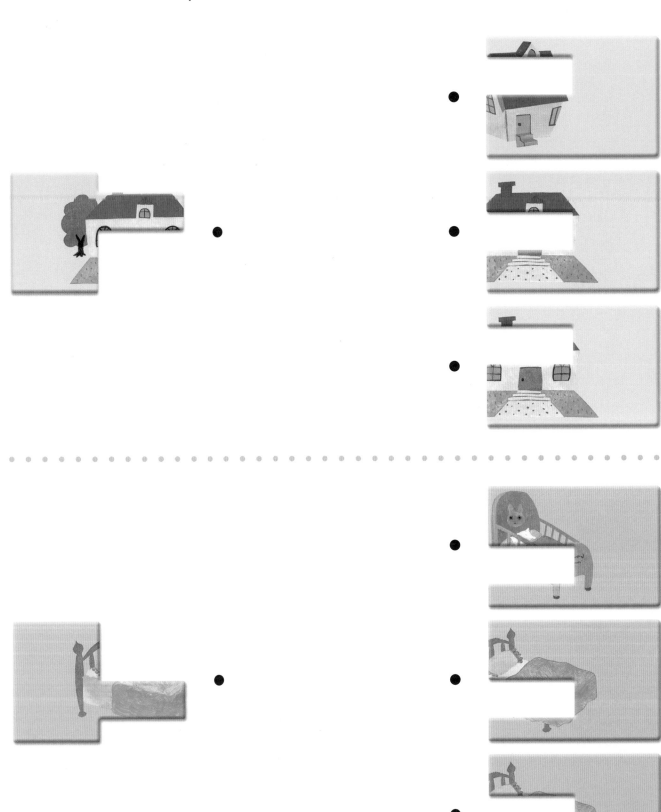

 **Jigsaw Puzzles**
Level Two

Name

Date

■ Draw a line to the piece that fits.

To parents
The three puzzle pieces in the right column have the same illustration. Encourage your child to look at the edge of each piece.

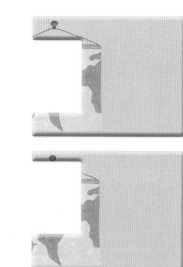

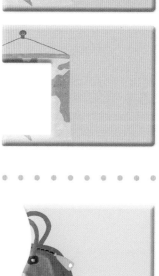

■ Draw a line to the piece that fits.

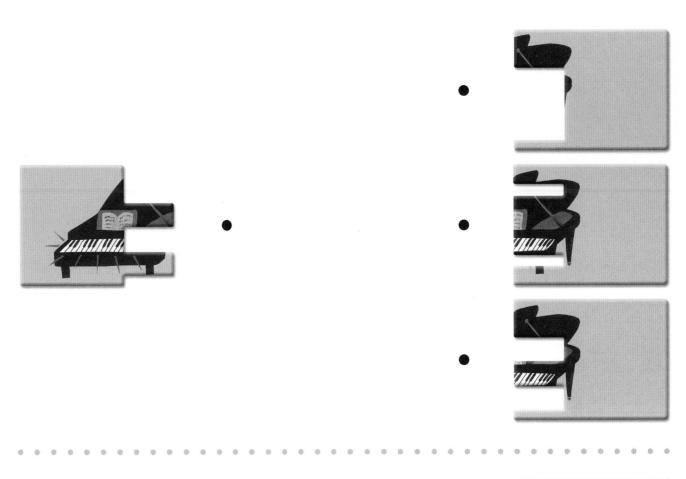

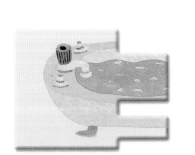

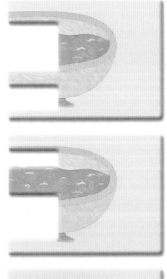

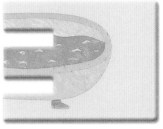

Jigsaw Puzzles
Level Three

Name

Date

■ Draw a line to the piece that fits.

To parents
The number of puzzle pieces has increased. Encourage your child to look carefully at each piece.

●

● ● ● ●

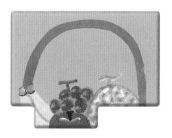

●

● ● ● ●

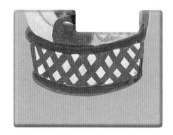 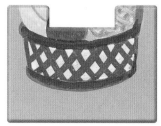  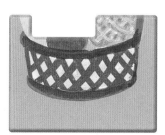

■ Draw a line to the piece that fits.

         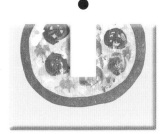

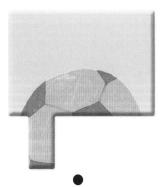

         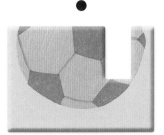

22

Jigsaw Puzzles
Level Four

Name

Date

■ Draw a line to the piece that fits.

To parents
If your child has difficulty with the activity, look at the edge of each puzzle piece with your child. Together, describe the shapes or patterns that you see.

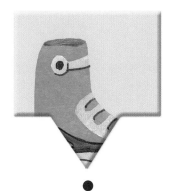

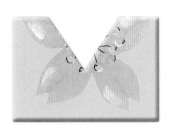

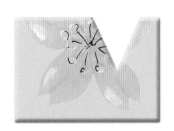

■ Draw a line to the piece that fits.

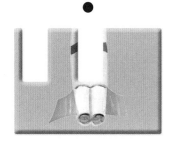
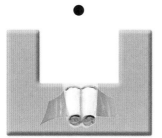
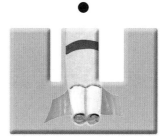

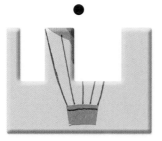
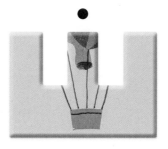
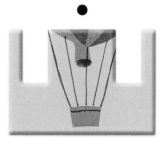

13 Matching Figures
Level One

■ Write a check mark (✓) above the matching animal.

To parents
If your child has difficulty with the exercise, look at the silhouette together. Ask your child to describe the features he or she sees.

( )   ( )   ( )

( )   ( )   ( )

■ Write a check mark (✓) above the matching animal.

26

Matching Figures
Level Two

Name

Date

■ Write a check mark (✓) above the matching animal.

To parents
When your child has completed the exercise, you may wish to have him or her explain how he or she chose the matching picture.

( )   ( )   ( )

( )   ( )   ( )

■ Write a check mark (✓) above the matching animal.

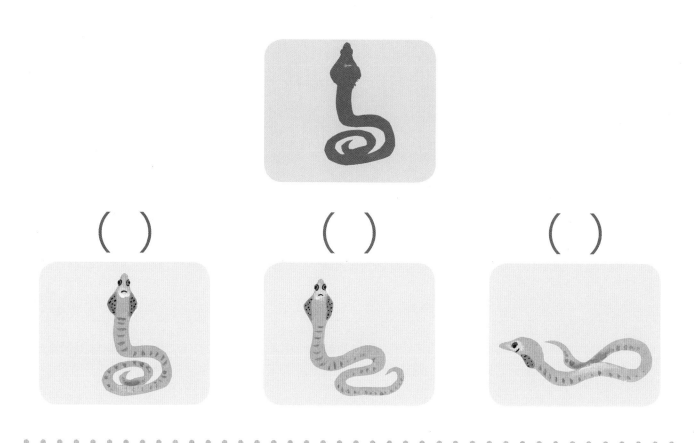

Matching Figures
Level Three

Name

Date

■ Write a check mark (✓) above the matching animal.

To parents
The number of illustrations in the bottom row has increased. Encourage your child to look carefully at each illustration.

( )   ( )   ( )   ( )

( )   ( )   ( )   ( )

■ Write a check mark (✓) above the matching animal.

( )   ( )   ( )   ( )

( )   ( )   ( )   ( )

Matching Figures
Level Four

Name

Date

■ Write a check mark (✓) above the matching animal.

To parents
Encourage your child to notice the details of each silhouette.

( )   ( )   ( )   ( )

( )   ( )   ( )   ( )

31

■ Write a check mark (✓) above the matching animal.

Copying Shapes

4 × 4 Dots

Name

Date

■ Draw the same shape.

To parents
Your child can start drawing from any dot he or she likes. The shapes in this section can be drawn without picking up the pencil, if your child would like to try.

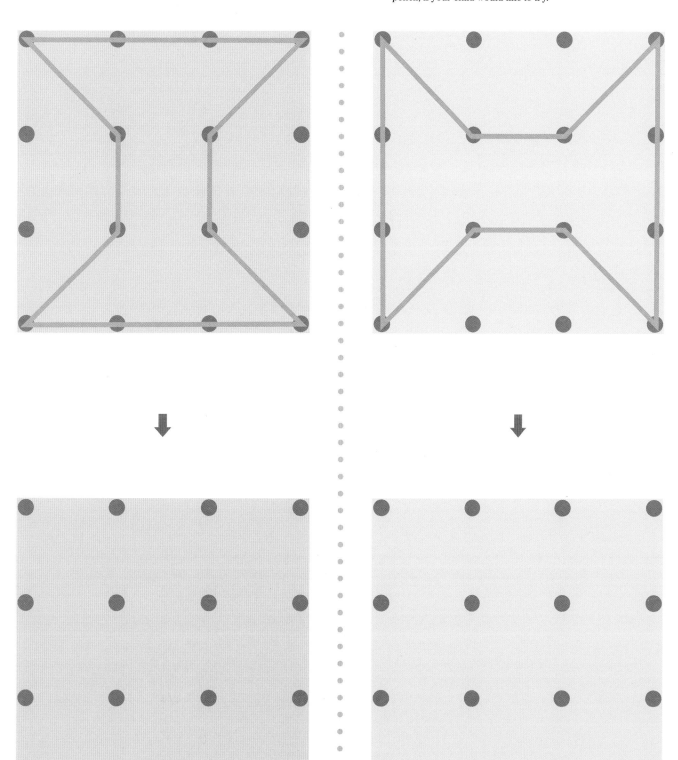

33

■ Draw the same shape.

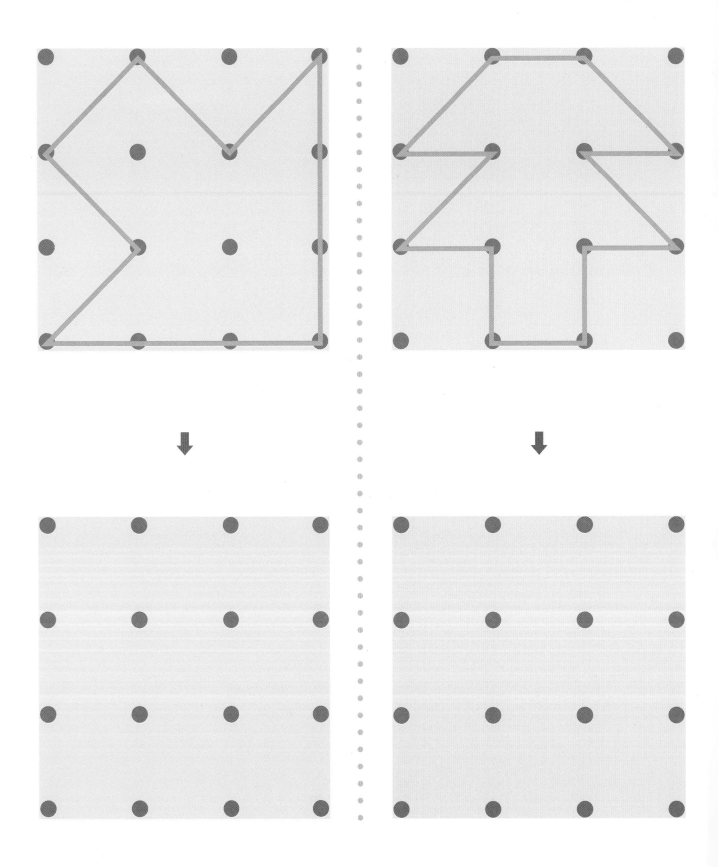

Copying Shapes
4 × 4 Dots

Name

Date

■ Draw the same shape.

To parents
If your child draws any of the lines incorrectly, encourage him or her to erase only the incorrect lines and to try again.

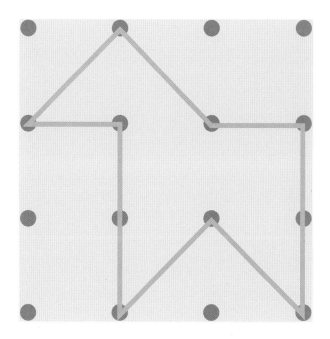

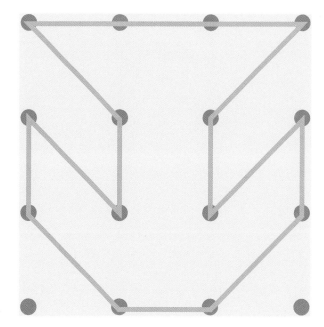

■ Draw the same shape.

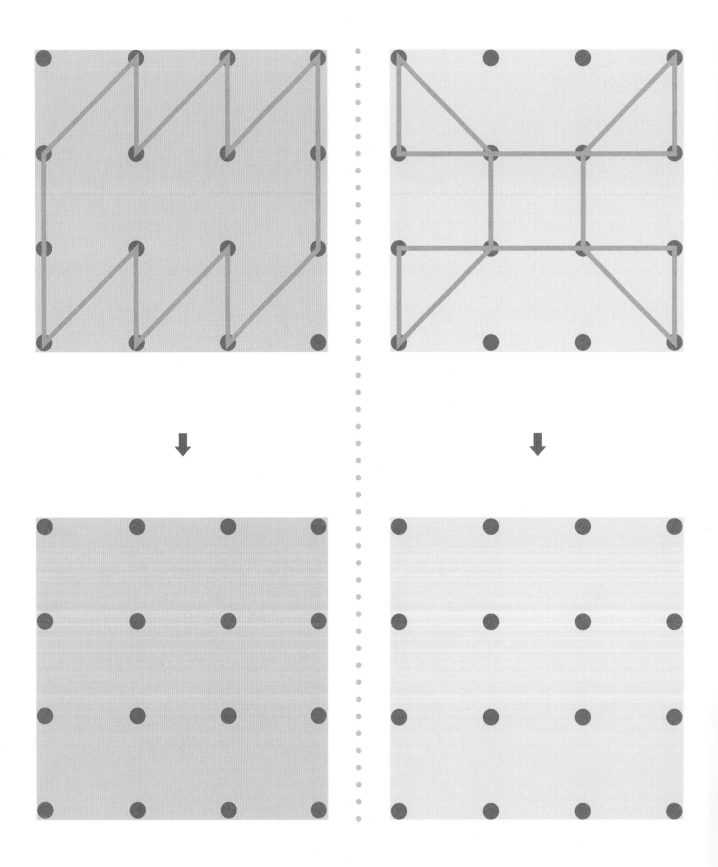

Copying Shapes

5 × 5 Dots

Name

Date

■ Draw the same shape.

To parents
The number of dots in the grid has increased. Guide your child to look carefully at the shapes before starting to draw.

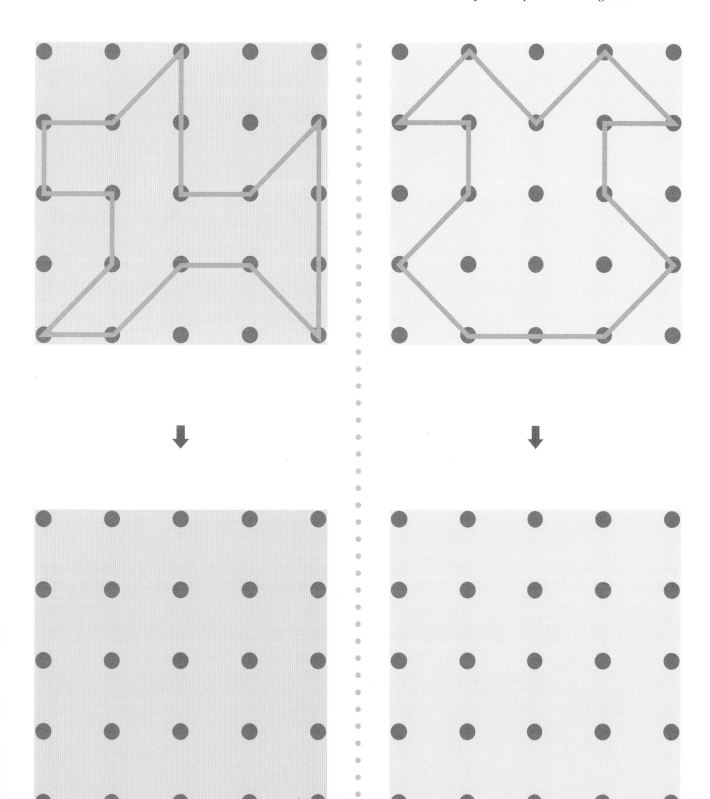

▪ Draw the same shape.

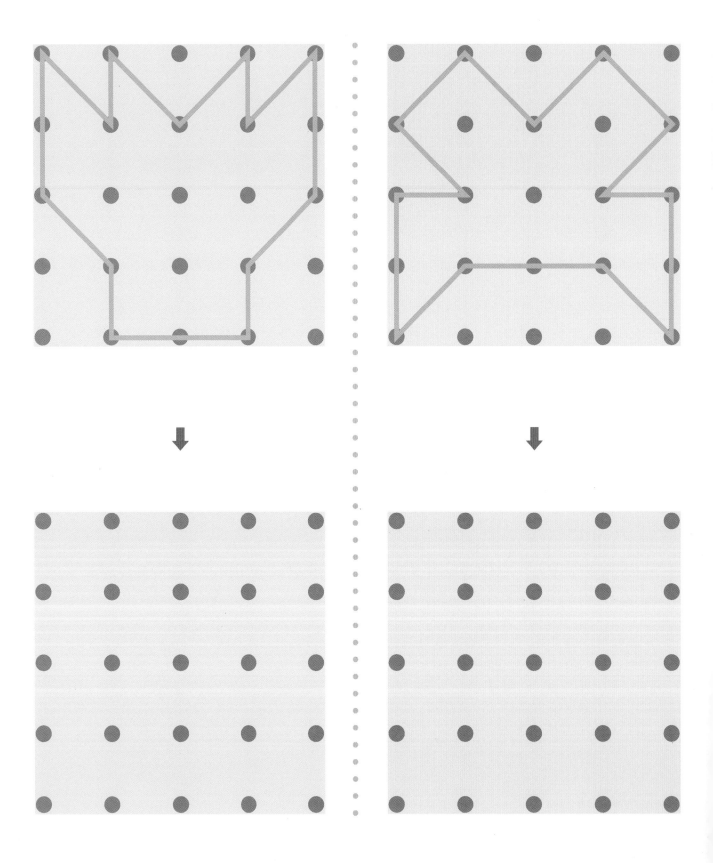

38

Copying Shapes
5 × 5 Dots

■ Draw the same shape.

Name

Date

To parents
From this point on, the shapes become more complicated. Give your child a lot of praise for his or her effort when your child finishes drawing.

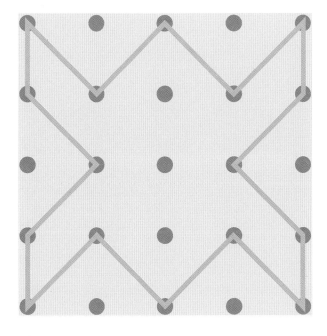

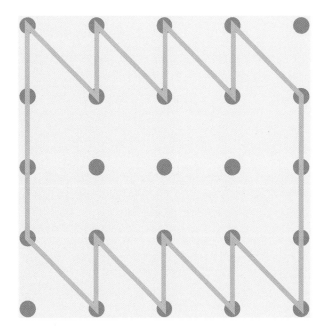

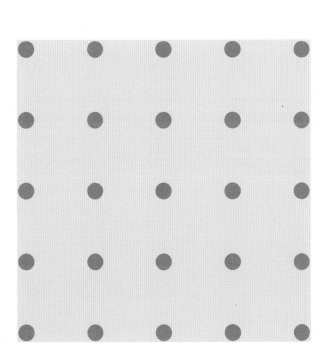

39

To parents
The shape in the right column on this page cannot be drawn without picking up the pencil.

■ Draw the same shape.

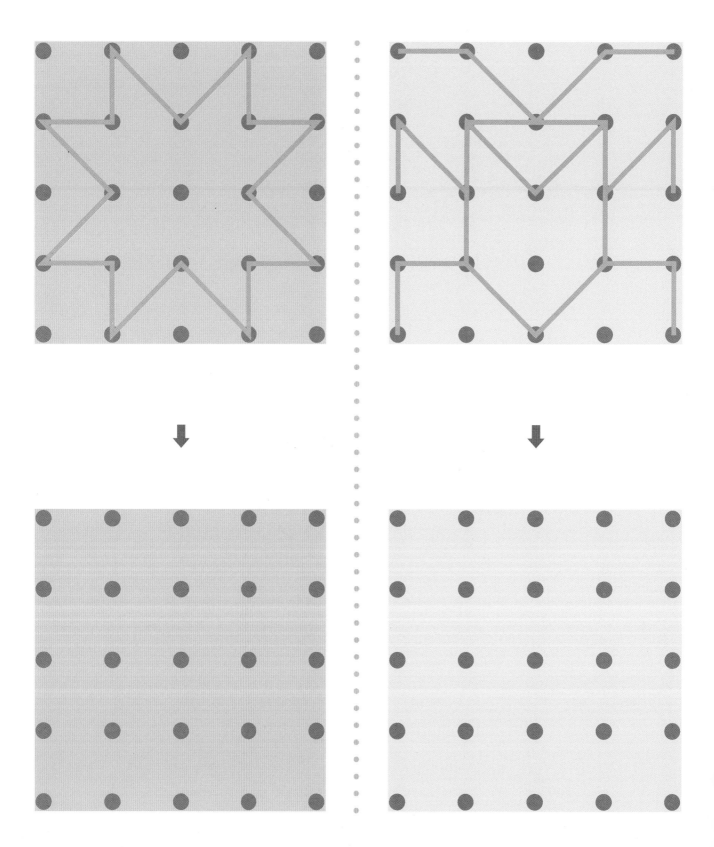

Above and Below
Level One

Name

Date

■ Which animal is above the flower?
Write a check mark (✓) beside the animal.

To parents
Before beginning this activity, you may wish to help your child recognize the words "above" and "below."

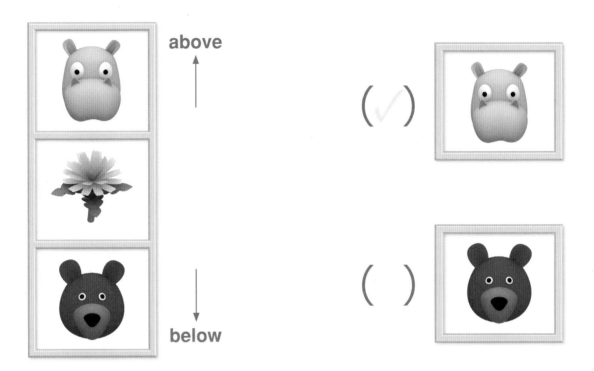

above

below

(✓)

( )

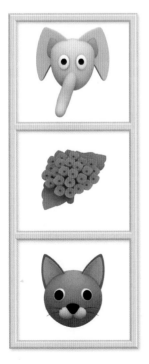

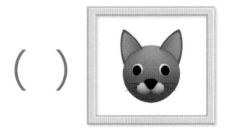

( )

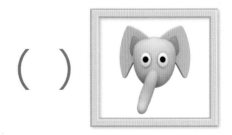

( )

41

■ Which animal is below the fruit? Write a check mark (✓) beside the animal.

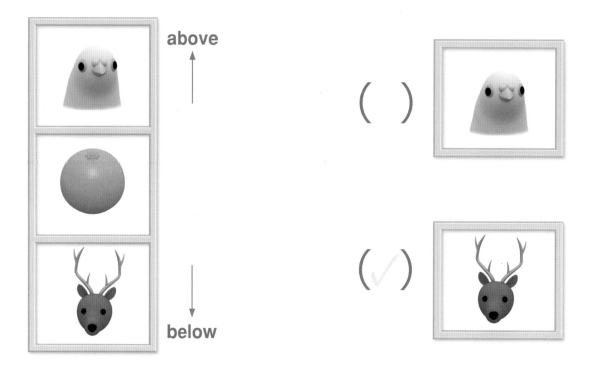

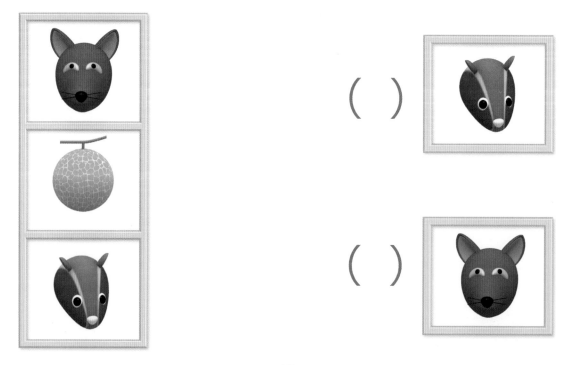

42

Above and Below
Level Two

Name

Date

■ Which animal is above the flower?
Write a check mark (✓) beside the animal.

To parents
The activity now includes pictures on all sides of
the flower. Encourage your child to choose the
correct animal.

43

■ Which animal is below the fruit? Write a check mark (✓) beside the animal.

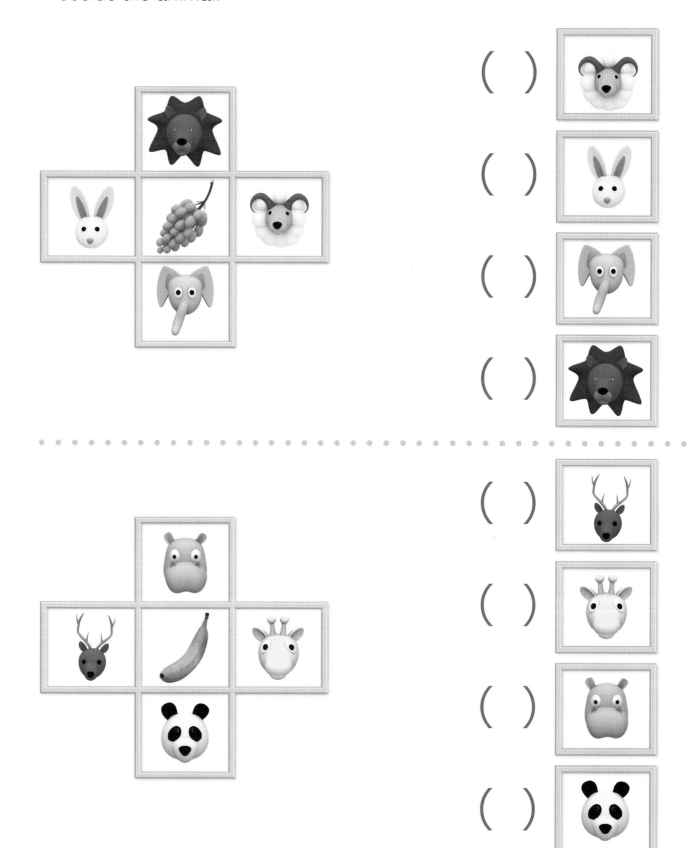

44

Above and Below
Level Three

Name

Date

■ Which animal is right above the flower?
Write a check mark (✓) beside the animal.

To parents
If your child has difficulty, help him or her understand the activity is similar to pages 41 and 42.

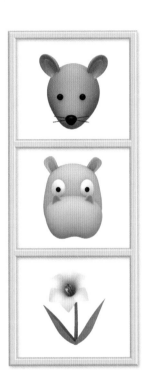

( )

( )

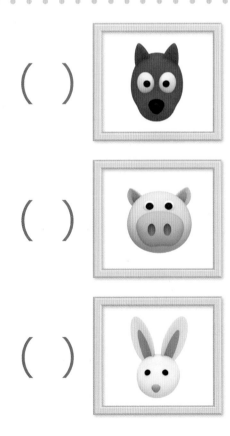

45

■ Which animal is right below the food? Write a check mark (✓) beside the animal.

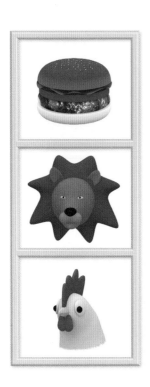

( )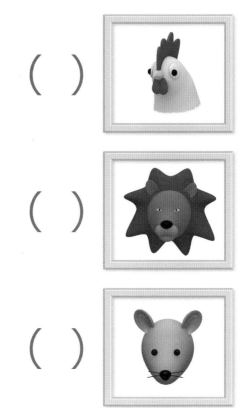

- -

( )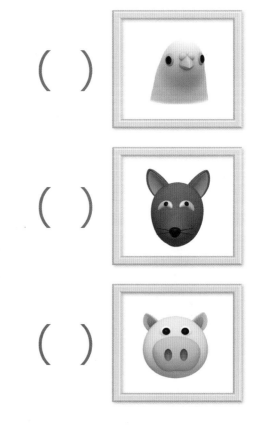

Above and Below
Level Four

Name

Date

■ Which animal is right above the flower?
Write a check mark (✓) beside the animal.

To parents
If your child has difficulty with the exercise, work with him or her to describe the animal above the flower.

( )

( )

( )

( )

( )

( )

( )

( )

■ Which animal is right below the fruit? Write a check mark (✓) beside the animal.

48

Right and Left
Level One

Name

Date

■ Which animal is to the right of the flower?
Write a check mark (✓) beside the animal.

To parents
Before beginning this activity, you may wish to help
your child recognize the words "left" and "right."

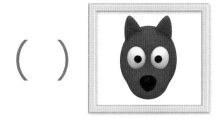

left ←——— ———→ right

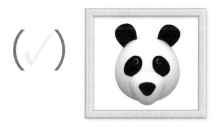

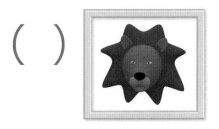

49

■ Which animal is to the left of the fruit? Write a check mark (✓) beside the animal.

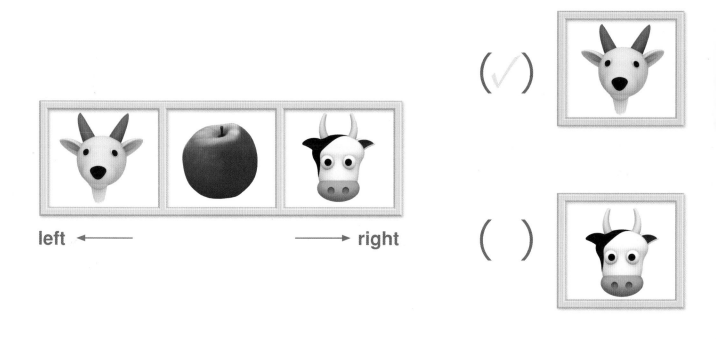

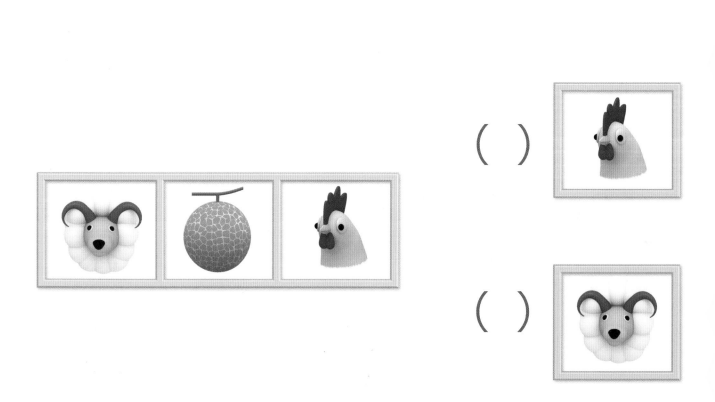

50

Right and Left
Level Two

Name

Date

■ Which animal is to the right of the flower?
Write a check mark (✓) beside the animal.

To parents
The activity now includes pictures on all sides of
the flower. Encourage your child to choose the
correct animal.

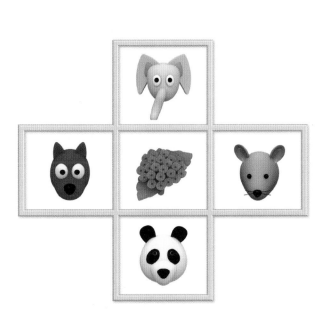

■ Which animal is to the left of the fruit? Write a check mark (✓)
 beside the animal.

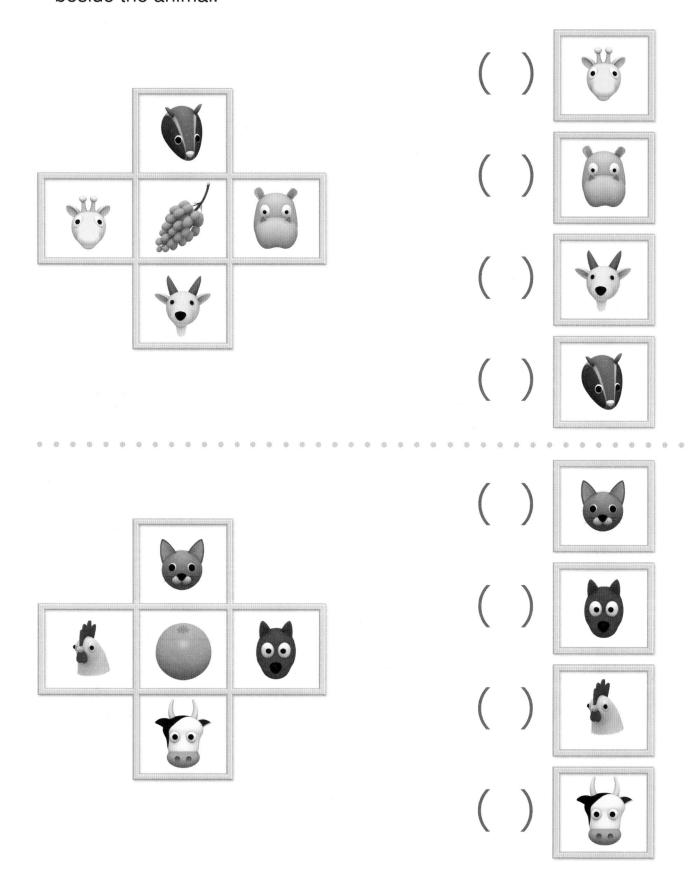

 **Right and Left**
Level Three

■ Which animal is to the right of the flower?
Write a check mark (✓) beside the animal.

To parents
If your child has difficulty, help him or her
understand the activity is similar to pages 49 and 50.

( )

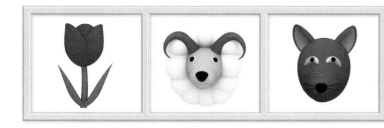

( )

( )

( )

( )

( )

53

■ Which animal is to the left of the food? Write a check mark (✓) beside the animal.

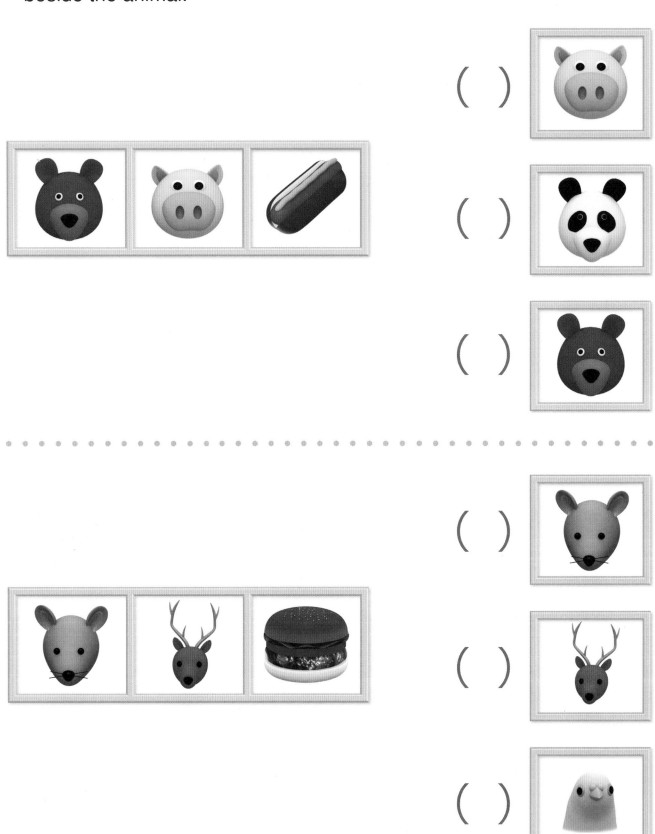

54

Right and Left
Level Four

Name

Date

■ Which animal is to the right of the flower?
Write a check mark (✓) above the animal.

To parents
If your child has difficulty with the exercise, work with him or her to describe the animal to the right of the flower.

( )   ( )   ( )   ( )

( )   ( )   ( )   ( )

55

■ Which animal is to the left of the fruit? Write a check mark (✓) above the animal.

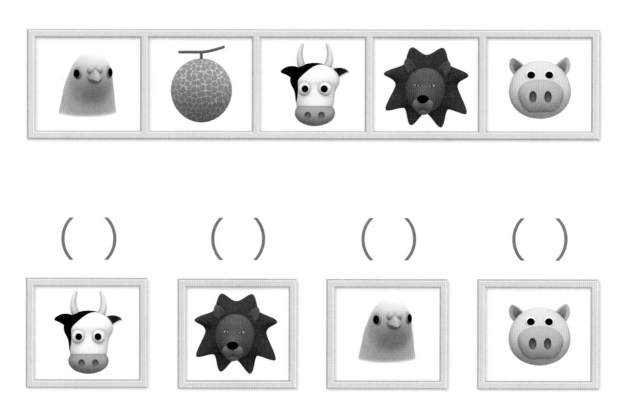

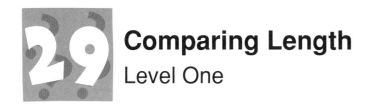

Comparing Length
Level One

Name

Date

To parents
Encourage your child to find the answer by looking closely at the pictures.

■ Look at the pictures. Then write a check mark (✓) above the object that is longer.

( )   (✓)

( )   ( )

■ Look at the pictures. Then write a check mark (✓) above the object that is longest.

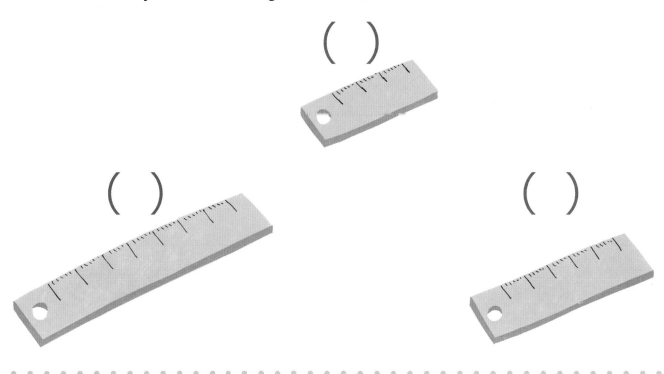

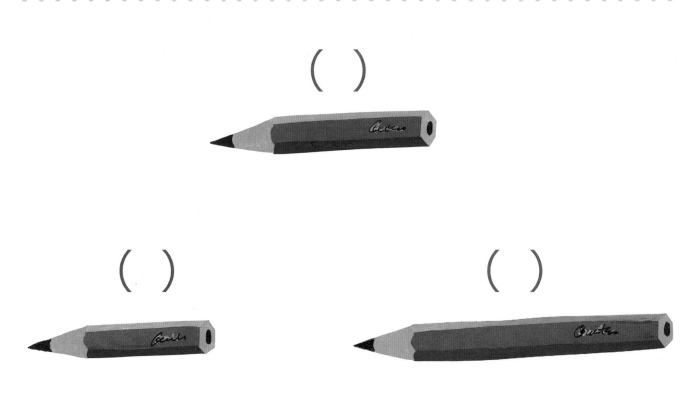

Comparing Length
Level Two

Name

Date

To parents
The number of pictures has increased. Encourage your child to compare all of the pictures.

■ Look at the pictures. Then write a check mark (✓) above the object that is longest.

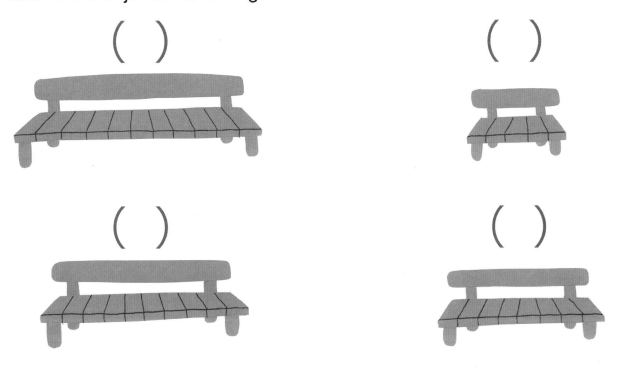

( )   ( )

( )   ( )

   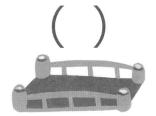

( )   ( )

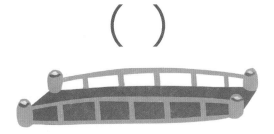   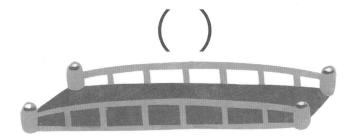

( )   ( )

■ Look at the pictures. Then write a check mark (✓) above the object that is longest.

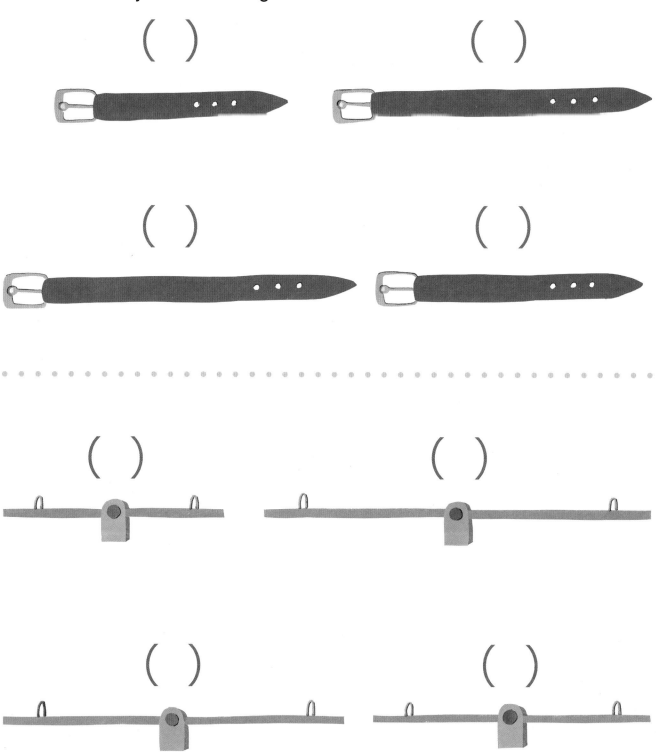

( )　　　　　　　　( )

( )　　　　　　　　( )

( )　　　　　　　　( )

( )　　　　　　　　( )

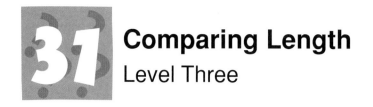

Name

Date

To parents
Encourage your child to think how long the objects would be if they were stretched out straight.

■ Look at the pictures. Then write a check mark (✓) above the object that is longer.

( )   (✓)

( )   ( )

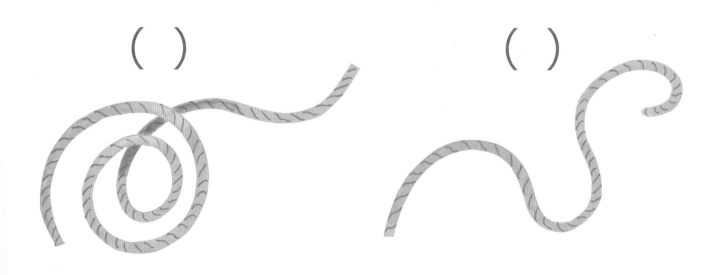

■ Look at the pictures. Then write a check mark (✓) beside the object that is longest.

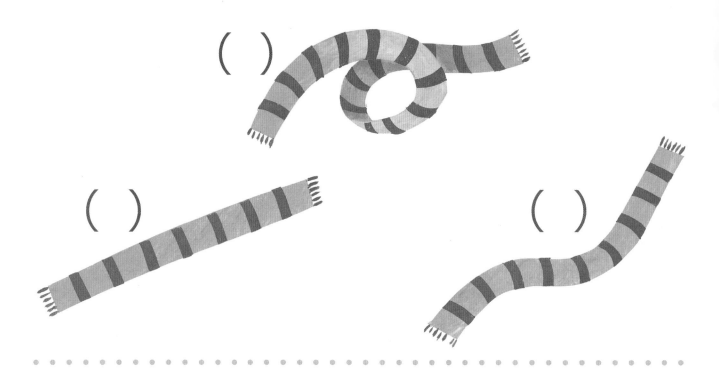

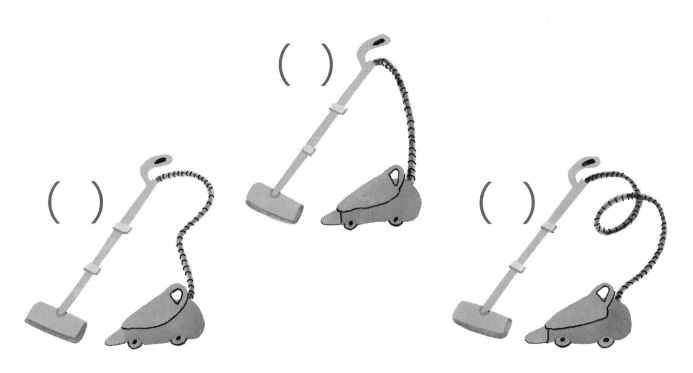

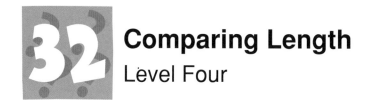

Comparing Length
Level Four

Name

Date

To parents
Give your child a lot of praise when he or she finds the right answer.

■ Look at the pictures. Then write a check mark (✓) under the object that is longest.

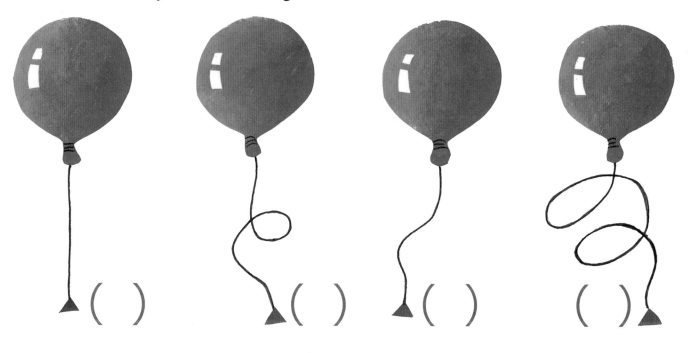

( )   ( )   ( )   ( )

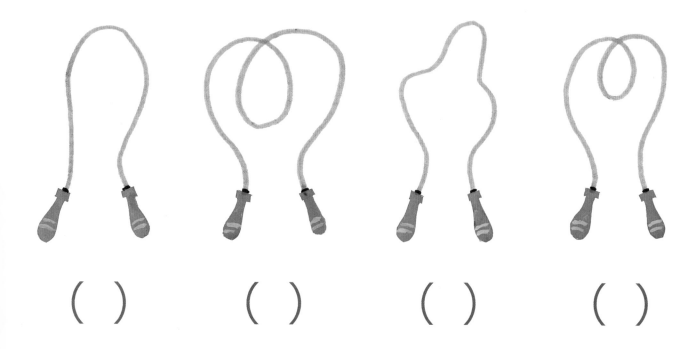

( )   ( )   ( )   ( )

■ Look at the pictures. Then write a check mark (✓) above the object that is longest.

( )   ( )   ( )   ( )

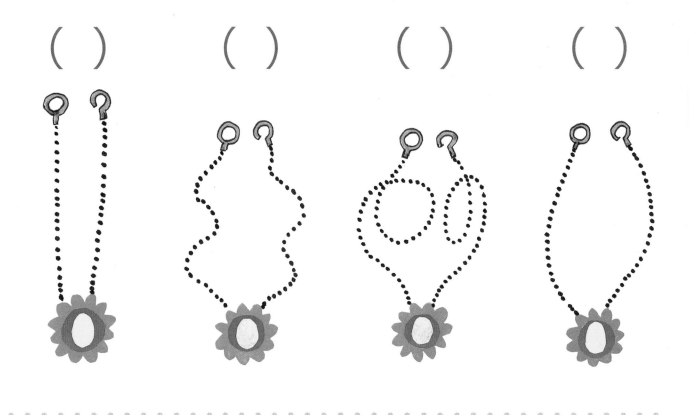

( )   ( )   ( )   ( )

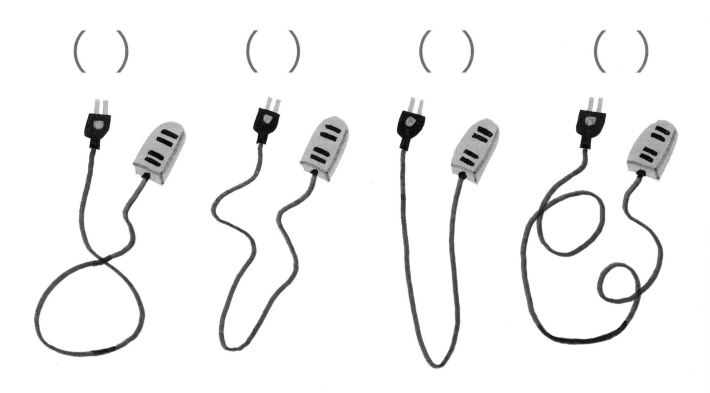

33 Coloring Patterns
Four Colors

Name

Date

■ Color each pattern with the correct color.

light blue → blue → yellow → red

To parents
From this page on, your child should use colored pencils. Give your child the colors listed in the instructions.

■ Color each pattern with the correct color.

Coloring Patterns
Five Colors

Name

Date

■ Color each pattern with the correct color.

→ light green → purple → light blue → green → red

To parents
Encourage your child to color the patterns in the picture, using the colors indicated.

Color each pattern with the correct color.

Coloring Patterns
Five and Six Colors

■ Color each pattern with the correct color.

→ blue　→ orange　→ yellow　→ black　→ purple

To parents
Encourage your child to color in each patterned area completely.

■ Color each pattern with the correct color.

Coloring Patterns
Six and Seven Colors

Name

Date

■ Color each pattern with the correct color.

→ red → light green → orange → light blue → purple → yellow

To parents
Help your child use the instructions to match up each pattern with the correct color.

Coloring Patterns Six and Seven Colors

To parents
This is the last exercise of this workbook. Please praise your child for the effort it took to complete this workbook.

■ Color each pattern with the correct color.

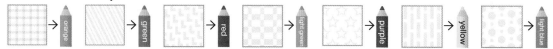

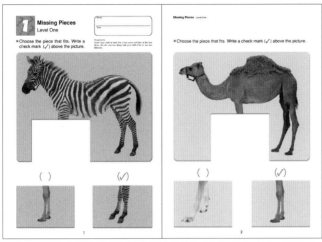

pages 1 and 2

pages 5 and 6

pages 3 and 4

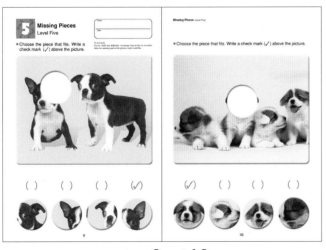

pages 9 and 10

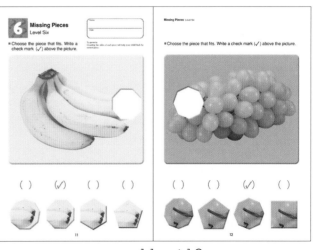

pages 11 and 12

pages 13 and 14

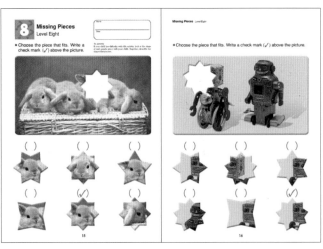

pages 15 and 16

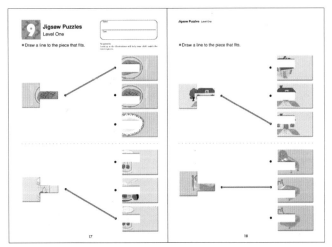

pages 17 and 18

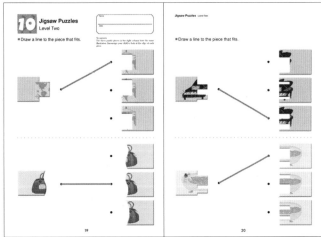

pages 19 and 20

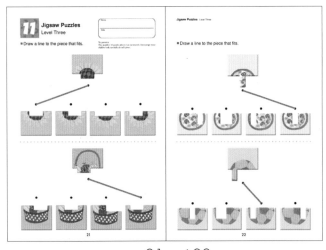

pages 21 and 22

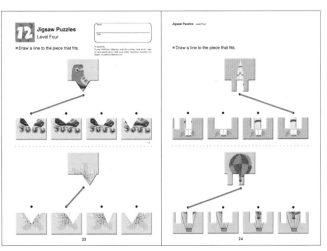

pages 23 and 24

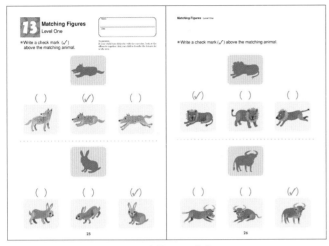

pages 25 and 26

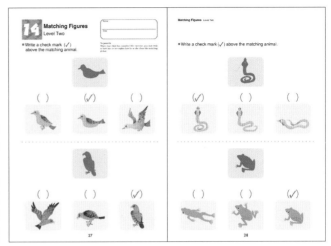

pages 27 and 28

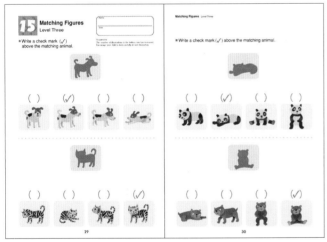

pages 29 and 30

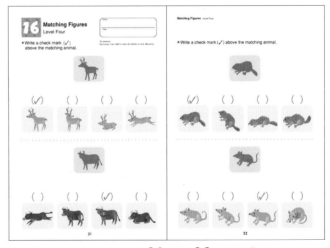

pages 31 and 32

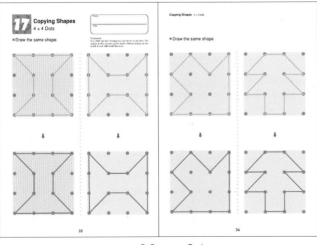

pages 33 and 34

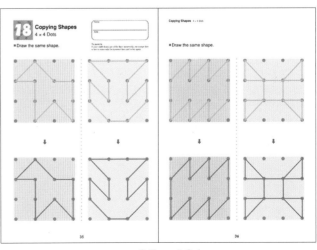

pages 35 and 36

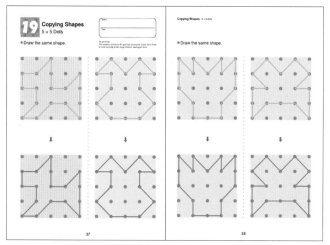

pages 37 and 38

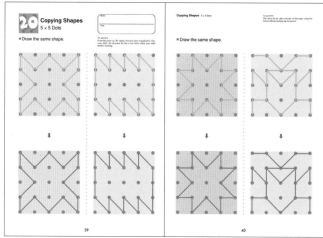

pages 39 and 40

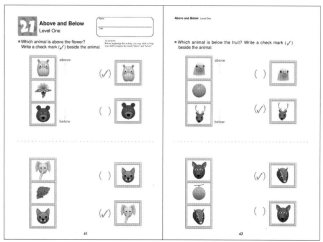

pages 41 and 42

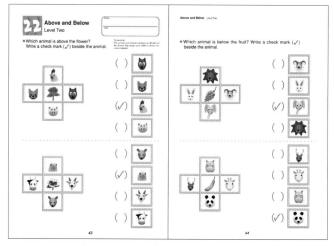

pages 43 and 44

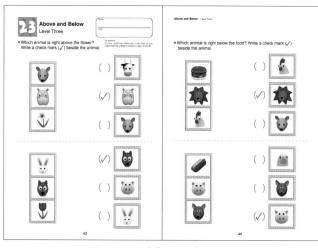

pages 45 and 46

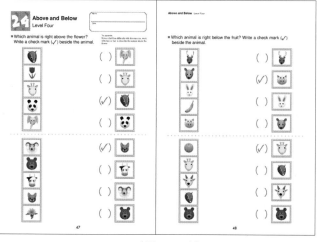

pages 47 and 48

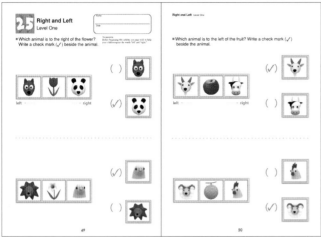

pages 49 and 50

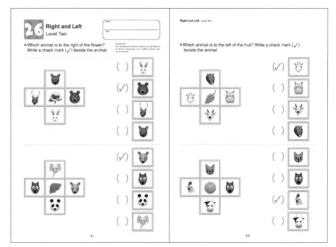

pages 51 and 52

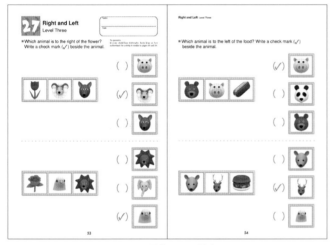

pages 53 and 54

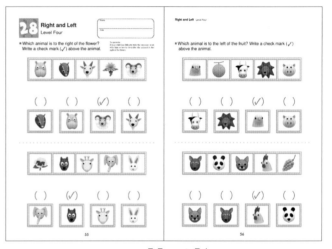

pages 55 and 56

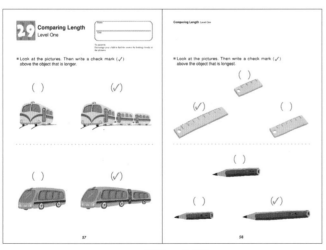

pages 57 and 58

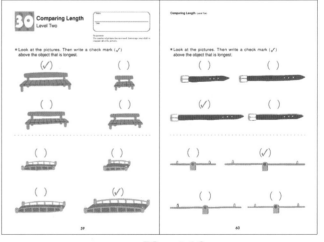

pages 59 and 60

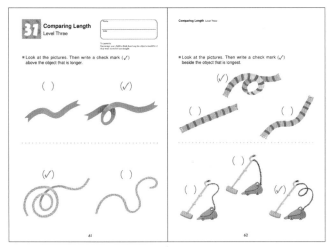

pages 61 and 62

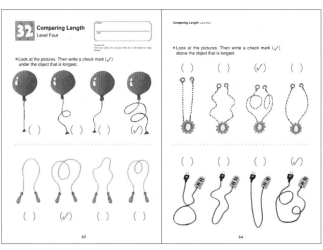

pages 63 and 64

pages 65 and 66

pages 67 and 68

pages 69 and 70

pages 71 and 72

Certificate of Achievement

....

is hereby congratulated on completing

Thinking Skills Workbooks
Kindergarten Spatial Reasoning

Presented on .... , 20 ....

....

Parent or Guardian

KUM◯N